武満 徹
フルートのための
巡り
イサム・ノグチの追憶に

TORU TAKEMITSU
ITINERANT

In Memory of Isamu Noguchi

for flute

SJ 1055

SCHOTT

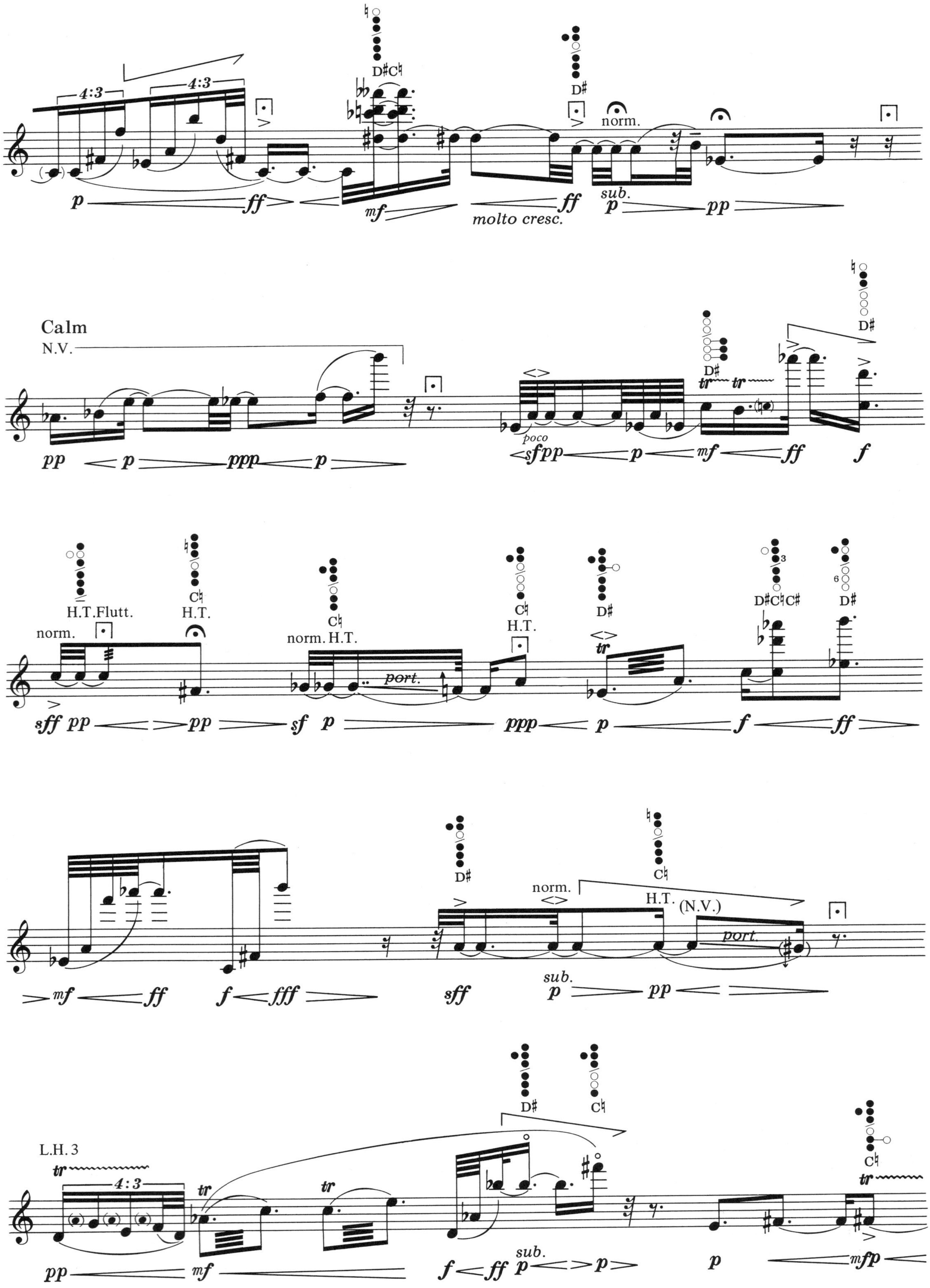
4:3
4:3
D♯C♮
D♯
norm.
molto cresc.
sub.
Calm
N.V.
poco
D♯
D♯
H.T.Flutt.
norm.
H.T.
C♮
norm. H.T.
port.
C♮
C♮
H.T.
D♯
D♯C♮C♯
D♯
D♯
C♮
norm.
H.T.
(N.V.)
port.
sub.
sub.
L.H. 3
4:3
D♯
C♮
sub.
C♮

Itinerant
—In Memory of Isamu Noguchi—
巡り
—イサム・ノグチの追憶に—
for flute

Toru Takemitsu
武満 徹

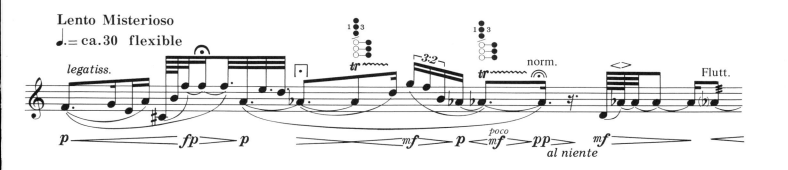

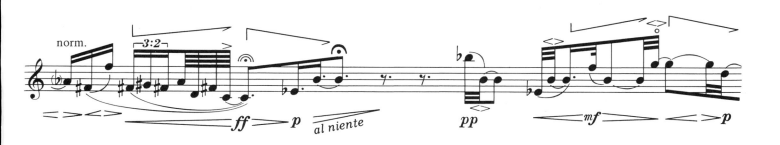

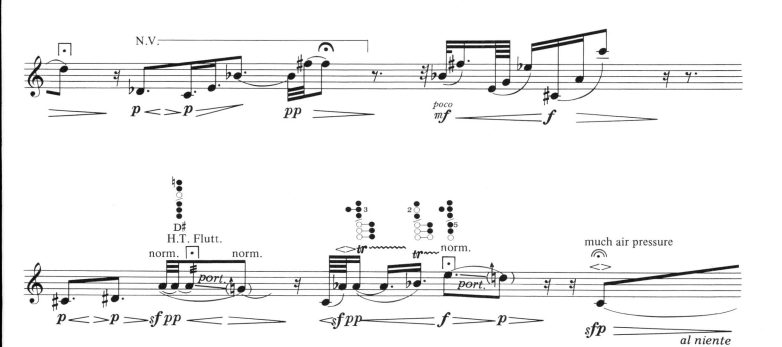

フルートのための《巡り》は、友人の彫刻家イサム・ノグチの死を悼んで作曲された。
初演はポーラ・ロビソンにより、1989年2月7日ニューヨークのイサム・ノグチ美術館でおこなわれた。

演奏時間—— 6 分

Itinerant for flute was composed to mourn the death of the composer's friend, the sculptor, Isamu Noguchi.
The first performance was given by Paula Robison at the Isamu Noguchi Museum in New York on February 7, 1989.

Duration: 6 minutes

NOTATION:

⌐ ⌒ ⌒	= Pauses of increasing duration (fermata: short, long, very long)
	= accelerando
	= ritardando
port.	= Make portamento
N.V.	= non vibrato
H.T.	= Hollow tone
norm.	= Normal playing (fingering)
Flutt.	= Flutter tonguing
	= Harmonics
♮	= Approximately 1/4 tone above
♭ ♮ ♯	= Approximately 1/4 tone below

Accidentals apply only to each note, except for tied notes.

FINGERING:

○	= Opened
●	= Closed
⦸	= Half closed
	= Alternate change of open (close) and close (open)

CHART OF FINGERING NUMBERS:

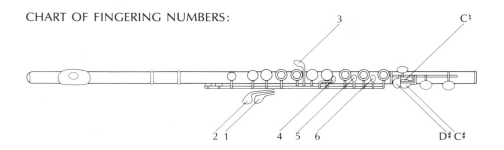

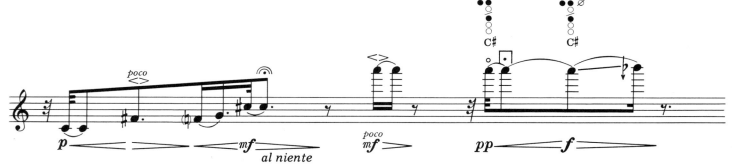

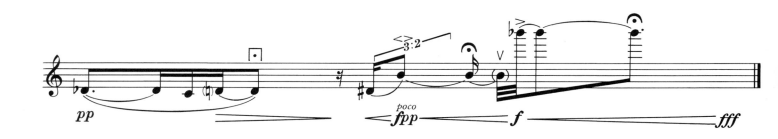

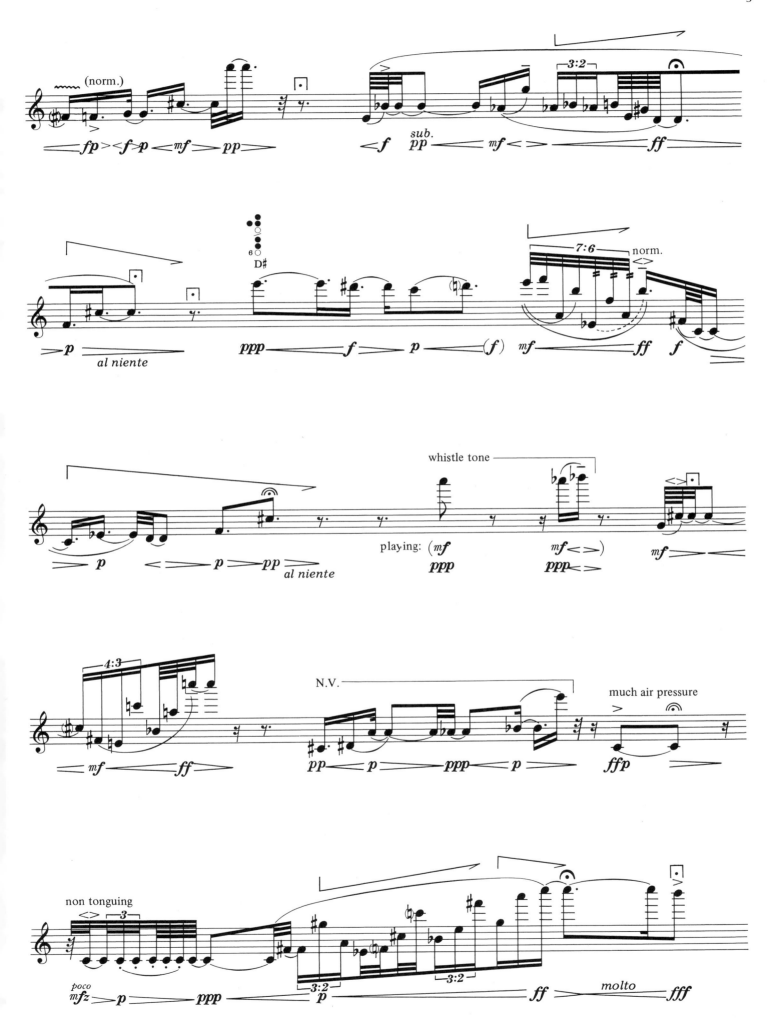

武満 徹《巡り》　　　　　　　　　　　　　●

フルートのための

初版発行————————————————1989年12月20日

第2版第6刷⑩————————————2019年3月25日

発行————————————————ショット・ミュージック株式会社

————————————————東京都千代田区内神田1-10-1 平富ビル3階

————————————————〒101-0047

————————————————(03)6695-2450

————————————————www.schottjapan.com

————————————————ISBN 978-4-89066-355-2

————————————————ISMN M-65001-092-4